HAMLET   LUCKY EDDIE   HÄGAR   HELGA   SNERT   HONI

HÄGAR

the horrible

on the rampage

RR
RAVETTE BOOKS

© 1991 King Features Syndicate, Inc.

This edition first published by Ravette Books Limited 1991

Printed and Bound
for Ravette Books Limited,
3 Glenside Estate, Star Road, Partridge Green,
Horsham, West Sussex RH13 8RA
An Egmont Company,
by Cox & Wyman Ltd, Reading

ISBN: 1 85304 314 1

A selection of HÄGAR books published by Ravette

POCKET BOOKS		BLACK AND WHITE LANDSCAPES	
TRIES AGAIN	£2.50	MEETS HIS MATCH	£2.50
HAS A GO	£2.50	IN A HURRY	£2.50
IN A FIX	£2.50		
ALL AT SEA	£2.50	COLOUR LANDSCAPES	
GETS IT ALL	£2.50	TELLS IT LIKE IT IS	£2.95
IN A STEW	£2.50	NEVER SAY DIE	£2.95
IN THE ROUGH	£2.50	MAKES AN ENTRANCE	£2.95
LEADS THE WAY	£2.50	WELCOME HOME	£2.95
TAKES A BREAK	£2.50		
ON HOLIDAY	£2.50	COLOUR THEME BOOKS	
TAKES AIM	£2.50	No. 1 THE GREAT GOURMET	£2.95
MEASURE FOR MEASURE	£2.50	No. 2 TROUBLE AND STRIFE	£2.95
SAYS IT WITH FLOWERS	£2.50	No. 3 TAKES A JOURNEY	£2.95
CHIPS AWAY	£2.50	No. 4 CHILD'S PLAY	£3.50
LOOKS HEAD	£2.50	No. 5 WHO DARES WINS	£3.50
ALBUMS		VIKING HANDBOOK	£3.95
THE HERO	£2.50		
LETS HIMSELF GO	£2.50		

All these books are available at your local bookshop or newsagent, or can be ordered direct from the publisher. Just tick the titles you require and fill in the form below. Prices and availability subject to change without notice.

Ravette Books Limited, 3 Glenside Estate, Star Road, Partridge Green, Horsham, West Sussex RH13 8RA

Please send a cheque or postal order and allow the following for postage and packing. UK: Pocket books – 45p for one book plus 20p for the second book and 15p for each additional book. Landscape series – 50p for one book plus 30p for each additional book. Other titles – 85p for one book plus 60p for each additional book.

Name ....

Address ....

....